EXPLORING
The God Question
STUDY GUIDE

written by

IAIN MORRIS

for use in conjunction with
The God Question DVD series

Published by Search For Truth Enterprises Ltd
www.searchfortruthenterprises.com

Edition 1 – *EXPLORING The God Question – Study Guide*

ISBN 978-0-9576023-0-4

Author – Iain Morris
Iain Morris' professional life encompasses the worlds of education and television and film production. He produced and directed this series of films. He is also a member of the board of the Search For Truth Charitable Trust.

Content:
Kharis Productions Ltd
Hamilton
www.kharisproductions.com

Typeset, Design and Distributed by:
Sanctus Media Ltd
Bo'ness
Tel: 01506 827217
www.sanctusmedia.com

See inside back pages for image copyright credits

Search for Truth Enterprises Ltd (Company No: SC344477)
is a subsidiary of Search for Truth Charitable Trust

Search for Truth Charitable Trust (Charity No: SC039465. Company No: SC340300) is a registered charity and private limited company registered in Scotland

WELCOME TO THE GOD QUESTION

THE GOD QUESTION PROVIDES AN OPPORTUNITY FOR VIEWERS TO **PARTICIPATE** IN AN **OPEN DISCUSSION** ABOUT WHETHER OR NOT **GOD EXISTS.**

WHAT IS AT STAKE IN THIS SERIES . . .

. . . IS WHETHER OUR MOST UP-TO-DATE SCIENTIFIC UNDERSTANDING OF THE UNIVERSE AND LIFE ON EARTH POINTS EITHER TO THE INVOLVEMENT OF A CREATOR OR A SERIES OF CHANCE HAPPENINGS INDEPENDENT OF A CREATOR.

IT IS THE BIGGEST QUESTION OF ALL

WHY DO WE BELIEVE WHAT WE BELIEVE?

Human beings are born 'believers' - about everything! It appears we are hard-wired to form beliefs even if sometimes our reasons for holding them are open to question.

Typically we pick up beliefs from others around; some beliefs might just be expressions of wishful thinking. Is it possible that, for some at least, belief in God could fall into one of these suspect categories? Is it feasible to pass on, generation after generation, beliefs which have not been carefully and objectively considered for decades?

More highly recommended is to think through the evidence for yourself. One contributor (Peter Atkins) describes God's existence as "the biggest question of all." If true, it is crucially important not only to know what you believe about God but why!

THE GOD QUESTION

The beginning of the 21st century has seen a rise, especially in Western culture, of cynicism about God and withering contempt for those who profess belief. Frequently, science is deployed by atheists as the chief weapon in their onslaught on belief. The underlying assumption is that what is real needs to be established by science alone; everything else is unreliable. Author of "The End of Faith", Sam Harris, describes faith as "the mother of all bad reasons"; Richard Dawkins simply claims God is "delusion".

The truth is crucially important if they're right; and arguably even more important if they're wrong.

THE GOD QUESTION AND YOU

The God Question series gives you a unique opportunity to think through, for yourself, important evidence for God's existence. Granted, it can neither be proved nor disproved but a well substantiated view can be formed on the balance of evidence.

But where might that evidence be found? Science itself is a vital source. It cannot tell us if there is a creator but it can offer pointers.

To probe further, this series investigates three 'worlds' of major interest to science:

THE COSMOS; LIFE ON EARTH; THE HUMAN MIND.

In each programme you will discover – at least in a general way – the scientific story, as far as each is known. You will also explore underlying questions such as 'where from?' and 'why?'

REACHING A VERDICT

The ultimate aim of this series is to provide you with information and reasoning on which you can base your own judgement about God's existence. To help you to do that openly and honestly, both sides of the argument are presented. A unique feature of The God Question series is that believers and non believers express their strongly held views – based on the same available evidence! It is for you to decide who has the stronger case.

Almost every contributor to the programmes is a highly respected expert in their field. They are brought to the screen for one specific purpose:

SO THAT THE FINAL VERDICT CAN BE YOURS.

The intended audience for the series comprises people of faith as well as people of no religious faith – indeed any who are searching. They are likely to have an interest in truth rather than choosing to maintain a position without testing its validity.

THE PROGRAMMES

THE GOD QUESTION IS A SERIES OF DOCUMENTARY FILMS WITH ACCOMPANYING STUDY GUIDE.

1. **EXPLORING THE GOD QUESTION**
   The Cosmos (Parts 1 and 2)

2. **EXPLORING THE GOD QUESTION**
   Life and Evolution (Parts 1 and 2)

3. **EXPLORING THE GOD QUESTION**
   Mind and Consciousness (Parts 1 and 2)

There is a connecting website – www.thegodquestion.tv – to encourage further investigation and to promote widespread conversation.

Programme 1 :
EXPLORING THE GOD QUESTION - THE COSMOS (PART 1)

WHAT IS AT STAKE IN THIS PROGRAMME...

...IS WHETHER SCIENTIFIC DISCOVERIES ABOUT THE BIRTH AND DEVELOPMENT OF OUR UNIVERSE SUGGEST THAT A CREATOR IS ESSENTIAL TO ITS SUCCESS – OR AS DISPENSABLE AS THE MYTHOLOGICAL GODS OF ANCIENT GREECE AND ROME.

INTRODUCING THE COSMOS

Debating the existence of God leads us to face ultimate questions. Chief among them is the question of where we came from. This programme explores what orthodox science believes about 'the beginning' and what happened next!

The belief that our universe came from the 'big bang' is well known and widely accepted. Often less appreciated, is that the 'big bang' resulted in order not chaos! That order was produced through a sequence of spectacular events that scientists believe led eventually to life being birthed on planet earth.

As these mysteries have been explored, there have been major advances in knowledge and understanding. However, important underlying questions remain – such as:

'Is science making God unnecessary or discovering the work of a creator?'

'Does the order in the universe provide evidence of God or not?'

These questions are not within the scope of science to answer
– yet it does provide crucial evidence.

In the 21st century, the subject of God's existence remains a 'hot topic'. This programme highlights the prominent ongoing debate between atheists and theists and, through investigating the wonders of the cosmos, asks if what we are learning through science appears to reduce the case for God's existence or, instead, supports it.

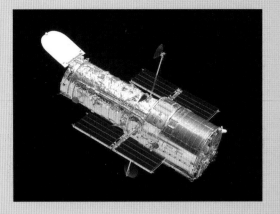

PROGRAMME 1 PART 1 : CONTENT GUIDE

This content guide is to help you follow the narrative of the programme as easily as possible. Each coloured dot appears on the screen to provide you with a cross reference.

1 Setting the scene.

2 We live in a universe of wonder! It calls for an explanation and inevitably raises the God question.

3 A long running public debate is taking place between atheists and theists about God's existence. Science has become an important battleground.

4 Many believers - aware of the threat coming from atheists' attempts to use science to discredit belief in God - are addressing and debating the question 'what evidence do we have for believing what we believe?'

5 The view that science and religion are in conflict has been around for centuries. The famous clash between Galileo and the Catholic church is a prime example. But was it really a conflict about science and God?

6 Centuries of scientific development and rational thinking have progressively eliminated gods that we know to have been imagined. The gods of ancient Greece and Rome are totally discredited. But the 'God of Abraham' continues to be worshipped in three world religions. Why?

7 Scientists have unravelled an extraordinary story about the history and development of our universe. It has progressed from what seemed to be chaos to something that works extraordinarily well. Is God the most rational explanation? Or something else?

 **PLAY** ▶ **VIEW PROGRAMME**

THE BIG ISSUES

? WHY DO **SCIENCE AND RELIGION** APPEAR, TO SOME, TO BE IN **CONFLICT?**

WHAT CONTRIBUTION HAS BEEN MADE BY NEW ATHEISTS SUCH AS **RICHARD DAWKINS**, AUTHOR OF 'THE GOD DELUSION'?

? DO THE CONCLUSIONS OF **CONTEMPORARY SCIENCE** ABOUT THE ORIGIN AND **DEVELOPMENT OF THE UNIVERSE** LEND SUPPORT TO BELIEF IN **GOD'S EXISTENCE** OR UNDERMINE IT?

? ACCORDING TO PETER ATKINS, THE EXISTENCE OF GOD IS **"ONE OF THE BIGGEST QUESTIONS OF ALL"**. DO YOU AGREE?

Programme 1 :

EXPLORING THE GOD QUESTION - THE COSMOS (PART 1)

FOR MORE IN-DEPTH DISCUSSION

INTERPRETING THE EVIDENCE

"I think contemporary cosmology is not merely consistent with the existence of a creator, I think it is actually supportive."

William Lane Craig

"That's the history of mysteries: they get solved by science; the gap goes away. The religious explanation that used to fill the gap disappears. Nobody makes the explanation anymore and that's the fate of it."

Michael Shermer

Who do you think is right?

THE ATHEIST CHALLENGE

"All those deep questions that religion once aspired to explain are now better, more grandly, in a more beautiful and elegant fashion, explained by science."

Richard Dawkins

"There is no evidence at all for believing there's any truth to it (religion)."

Christopher Hitchens

"Wasting your time being wrong is the modus operandi (normal practice) of religion."

Sam Harris

The quotations above state some of atheism's criticisms of religious faith.

To what extent do you think these criticisms are valid?

How would you respond to them?

QUESTION 1

QUESTION 2

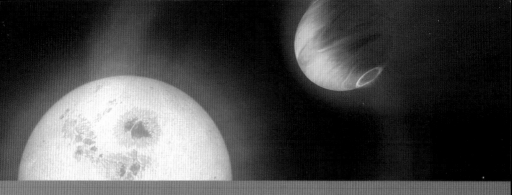

FACING UP TO THE CHALLENGE

"There's no point in ducking it. We need to face up to the issues because truth is one of the great Christian claims."

Rev Hugh Palmer

Has the church had a tendency to 'duck' the issues raised by those who are hostile to religion?
If so, why?

What risks are there in opening up your own beliefs to scrutiny? Are they worth taking?

THE GALILEO INCIDENT

"He set the earth on its foundations; it can never be moved."

Psalm 104:5

"Galileo took up a scientific question but then encountered problems because he wanted to be a bit of a theologian."

Father Rafael Pascual

How do you think the Galileo incident affected the reputation of the church?

Galileo's clash with the church involved the interpretation of Bible verses which were taken to mean that the earth literally stands still. Do you think that there is a real conflict between modern science and certain passages from the Bible (like the one above)? Is it mostly a question of interpretation? Can science ever be wrong?

QUESTION 3 QUESTION 4

WHAT KIND OF GOD?

"When most people use the word 'God', they have in mind a sort of miracle-working superbeing, a type of cosmic magician."

Paul Davies

"Newton...didn't say 'now I understand how the universe works; I don't need God'... He said 'What a marvellous God who did it that way'."

John Lennox

How is the God of the first statement different from the second?

How do these contrasting views affect the science/God debate?

THE BIG BANG

"The Big Bang is as certain as anything in science."

Steven Weinberg

"It is a big mystery as to how the Big Bang went 'bang' and produced such orchestrated uniformity because if you put a stick of dynamite in a pile of bricks – bang! You've got a total mess!"

Paul Davies

"If the elements (helium and hydrogen) had formed not at the end of 3 minutes but at the end of 30 seconds . . . it would be a very different universe."

Steven Weinberg

The history of the universe presents many mysteries and surprises. For example: order came from an 'explosion'; crucial timing produced just the right balance of helium and hydrogen for us to exist.

Do you think such factors have any relevance to discussion about the existence of God?

QUESTION 5

QUESTION 6

A FAVOURED PLANET?

"Earth, for some reason, found itself at a distance from the star . . . that it allowed for liquid water to exist on its surface."

Mario Livio

"It's really just chance."

Steven Weinberg

"Are we simply specs of dust or is there something quite different and special about human beings?"

David Wilkinson

All are agreed that earth seems to have a remarkably favoured position in the solar system. Could this just be chance?

MEANING AND PURPOSE

"What's the significance of human beings in such a vast cosmos?"

David Wilkinson

"Do we live in a universe that's about something?"

Paul Davies

"It does raise the question: Is that just a bit of luck or is there something going on in cosmic history?"

John Polkinghorne

Are there features of our universe that, in your opinion, suggest meaning and purpose?

QUESTION 7   QUESTION 8

Programme 1 :
EXPLORING THE GOD QUESTION –
THE COSMOS (PART 2)

WHAT IS AT STAKE IN THIS PROGRAMME...

...IS WHETHER SCIENTIFIC DISCOVERIES ABOUT THE BIRTH AND DEVELOPMENT OF OUR UNIVERSE SUGGEST THAT A CREATOR IS ESSENTIAL TO ITS SUCCESS - OR AS DISPENSABLE AS THE MYTHOLOGICAL GODS OF ANCIENT GREECE AND ROME.

SPECIFICALLY IN PART 2...

Is our universe, with all its precision necessary to support life, more likely to be the result of chance or the work of a creator?

PROGRAMME 1 PART 2 : CONTENT GUIDE

This content guide is to help you follow the narrative of the programme as easily as possible. Each coloured dot appears on the screen to provide you with a cross reference.

1 A reminder of key points raised in Part 1.

2 Theists and atheists clash on some big issues related to the God question. The key issues are:

- Isn't the existence of a creator just patently obvious?

- Is the universe mostly just 'a waste of stuff'?

- How could 'something' come from 'nothing' without a creator?

- Who created God?

- Centuries ago, the Bible stated that the universe had a beginning. Only in the last hundred years has science confirmed it. Does this enhance the Bible's credibility?

3 Much of the apparent conflict between science and God comes from the biblical account of six day creation. Some theists argue there need be no conflict.

4 Atheists recognise they must find an explanation of how a universe could come into existence without a creator. They are proposing the 'multiverse' concept. Is it a credible alternative?

5 Science has shown the universe to be extraordinarily fine tuned for life. Does this point to the existence of a 'fine tuner' or are we winners in a cosmic lottery?

6 Theists face up to the challenge that God as an explanation is just filling a gap that will later be replaced by scientific knowledge.

7 Drawing a conclusion: your decision!

 PLAY **VIEW PROGRAMME**

THE BIG ISSUES

? THE **UNIVERSE** APPEARS TO BE **FINE TUNED FOR LIFE**. IS THIS A CONVINCING ARGUMENT FOR THE **EXISTENCE OF GOD?**

? DOES THE **MULTIVERSE CONCEPT** UNDERMINE **THE CASE FOR GOD?**

? CAN THE **BIBLICAL CREATION STORY** SQUARE WITH OUR CURRENT UNDERSTANDING OF **COSMOLOGY?**

21

Programme 1 :

EXPLORING THE GOD QUESTION – THE COSMOS (PART 2)

FOR MORE IN-DEPTH DISCUSSION

WHO MADE GOD?

"If you posit a God that started it, I can just say: 'who created God?' "

Michael Shermer

"God is a being who exists without being explained by anything outside of God himself."

John Polkinghorne

Which of these positions do you find more convincing?

NOTE ON QUESTION 2

One of the main sources of conflict between science and religion has emerged from disputes about the timescale involved in the creation and development of the universe.

Using mathematics and sophisticated (though arguably not infallible) dating methods, most scientists believe the universe began more than 13.7 billion years ago and that the earth formed about 4.7 billion years ago.

Some believers think that the opening chapter of the Bible shows a very different timescale.

This position, often described as "Young Earth Creationism", takes the six day timescale of Genesis 1 literally and stands in opposition to orthodox science on this issue.

QUESTION 1

RECKONING WITH GENESIS

"Faith and science ought not to conflict if both are means of discovering truth about reality. I think that the impression that there is a conflict has largely arisen because of literalistic interpretations of the opening chapter of the book of Genesis. . . . That viewpoint has been exploded by modern science."

William Lane Craig

How do you respond to William Lane Craig's view on this issue?

Do arguments about timescales obscure more important issues – such as the evidence in contemporary science for the involvement of a creator?

Are there lessons to be drawn from the 'Galileo incident' about the dangers of dogmatism in scriptural interpretation? Should scientists also be cautious of dogmatism?

A FINE-TUNED UNIVERSE

"We have found even a language, in this case mathematics, where we are able to express what the universe is doing and even make predictions."

Mario Livio

"If it (the universe) wasn't balanced in just that way, life wouldn't exist."

David Wilkinson

What, if anything, do the above statements contribute to the debate on the God question?

QUESTION 2   QUESTION 3

THE MULTIVERSE

If God - as creator of a universe just right for our kind of life - is rejected, then some other explanation has to be found.

Some scientists have suggested the idea of 'multiverse.' This is the proposition that, somewhere and by some means, millions of universes have emerged.

Out of the millions that might have come into existence, perhaps our universe was the only one that possessed all the laws necessary to produce our kind of life.

If so, perhaps we are alive because we were fortunate to be in the one universe that is just right for us.

"The principle of the multiverse provides at least an interim satisfying explanation in a way that a creator could not possibly be a satisfying explanation."

Richard Dawkins

"To get this to work, we still have to have some physics in the multi-verse... we still have to have a universe-generating mechanism... we still have to have some means of distributing laws among the universes that get created."

Paul Davies

"It is possibly evidence of the desperation of some people because the multiverse theory has become enormously popular – as if it's either God or a multiverse! They forget it could be both!"

John Lennox

How do you think the multiverse concept/argument affects the case for God?

QUESTION 4

IN CONCLUSION

"The theist like myself would say, as we look at the beauty and elegance of the laws of physics, I think we see something of a creator God. But that revelation is not proof. Each of us can make a judgment on how we interpret that evidence."

David Wilkinson

Although we can't disprove there's a God, it is very...unlikely indeed.

Richard Dawkins

Do you think the existence/non existence of God can be proved?

Do you think a convincing case for the existence of God can be made from what science reveals about the Cosmos? Does any of the evidence seem to point in the opposite direction?

For a summary of *The Case for Theism / The Case for Atheism*, see Appendix 1.

QUESTION 5

IN SUMMARY, CONTEMPORARY SCIENCE has concluded that all matter that would ever exist in the universe came from a tiny dot that suddenly grew. The laws of physics shaped a universe which provided conditions for life on planet earth.

Science itself is based on the assumption, never contradicted, that the universe is intelligible and can be understood. As science has progressed, the level of precision and balance in the forces shaping the universe and supporting life has been discovered to be truly astonishing. How are these scientific discoveries to be interpreted?

IN SUMMARY, THE CASE FOR THEISM is that something (including a universe) cannot come from nothing. Even if there was a chain of events, there must exist somewhere an uncreated 'first cause' which is beginningless and timeless. God is the only reasonable explanation. Furthermore, the existence of universal laws supports the thesis that there is a law giver; the operational precision which is found in the universe points to there being a fine tuner.

Consequently it is reasonable to conclude that the emergence of life was an intention built into the universe from the very beginning. The creator God is not a substitute for circumstances we don't understand but rather the ultimate explanation as to why anything exists at all.

SCIENCE IS NOT IN CONFLICT WITH BELIEF IN GOD: IT REVEALS THE CREATOR'S METHOD.

Science is not in conflict with belief in God: it reveals the Creator's method.

IN SUMMARY, THE CASE FOR ATHEISM is that God is not helpful as an explanation. It raises the question 'who made God?' Besides, the role of science is to seek non theistic explanations. Admittedly the origin of our universe remains a deep mystery but it is argued that our universe might be only one among millions of universes. Only a universe possessing the ability to survive would endure.
We happen to live in such a universe. We are, in a sense, winners in a cosmic lottery. Within this universe, by chance, planet earth emerged with all the potential necessary for life to develop, including being the right distance from the sun so allowing liquid water to exist. Once life had begun, evolution took over. There is no need for a creator.

MIGHT **OUR UNIVERSE** BE ONLY **ONE** AMONG **MILLIONS?**

APPENDIX 2: UNDERSTANDING THE TERMS

Although every attempt is made to keep scientific explanations as simple as possible, the use of some technical, or less familiar, terms is inevitable.

AGNOSTIC: A person, having no active belief in God, uncertain whether or not God exists, and perhaps even believing the truth about God's existence cannot be known.

ATHEIST: A person who explicitly denies the existence of any gods.

BIG BANG: This is the dominant theory of the beginning of the universe. It states that the universe began from an initial point (sometimes called a singularity) which has expanded over billions of years to form the universe as we now know it.

COSMOS: The universe, with all its space, galaxies and stars, especially when considered as an orderly and harmonious whole.

DARK ENERGY: A form of energy that is assumed to permeate all of space and increases the rate of expansion of the universe. It is hypothetical because it cannot be observed but is used to account for the differences between theory and observed results of gravity on matter that can be seen.

DARK MATTER: A form of matter which cannot be detected but is assumed to be present in the universe. The existence of dark matter is inferred from the effect of gravity on visible matter, such as stars and galaxies.
Note: Scientists have estimated that there is, ~70% dark energy, ~25% dark matter, but only ~5% 'normal' matter in our universe.
http://science.nasa.gov/astrophysics/focus-areas/what-is-dark-energy/

ELEMENTS: Chemically the simplest substances and so cannot be broken down further using chemical methods.
Note: Hydrogen is the most abundant element in the universe at 75% , followed by helium 23% and oxygen at 1%. The other elements make up the remaining 1%. In the earth's crust, oxygen (47%) is the most abundant element, followed by silicon 28%) and aluminium (8%). Dry air at sea level contains about 21% oxygen, 78% nitrogen and 1% argon.

FINE-TUNING: The conditions that allow life in the universe can only occur when certain universal fundamental constants lie within a very narrow range. (Hence the term fine-tuned.) If any of several constants were slightly different the universe would be unable to develop matter, astronomical structures or life on earth as it is presently understood.

FUNDAMENTAL CONSTANTS: The physical constants which play a fundamental role in the basic theories of physics (including the speed of light, the gravitational constant, electronic charge, electronic mass, Planck's constant etc) .

GALAXY: Any of a vast number of star systems held together by gravitational attraction usually in a symmetrical shape. The solar system is part of the Milky Way galaxy.

GOD OF THE GAPS: The phrase "God of the gaps" is used to describe attempts by some to justify the rationality of believing in God by pointing to perceived "gaps" in scientific knowledge, the danger being that as science advances there is less and less space for God.

GRAVITY (LAW OF UNIVERSAL GRAVITATION): This is the name given to the force of attraction that exists between objects (mass) in the universe. Without gravity, objects would not be held in place. The law may be technically expressed as follows: Every mass in the universe attracts every other mass with a force that is directly proportional to the product of their masses and inversely proportional to the square of the distance separating them.

($F = \dfrac{Gm_1m_2}{d^2}$ where G is the gravitational constant.)

LAWS OF PHYSICS: These scientific generalisations help explain consistency and order in the universe. They are based on many direct observations of physical behaviour and have become accepted universally within the scientific community. They are typically simple, absolute, universal and true in the sense that there have never been repeatable contrary observations.

MULTIVERSE: The idea that a hypothetical vast array of (multiple) universes (including our own) might exist. This is based on an unsubstantiated theoretical mathematical framework. It is unclear how this idea can actually be applied or verified scientifically, so it is controversial among many physicists.

PLANET: A planet is a spherical ball of rock and/or gas that orbits a star. Earth is a planet albeit a rather special one.

QUANTUM MECHANICS: The theory attempts to explain the peculiar behaviour of matter and energy in the world of the atom (the sub-atomic level). It is a world apparently with rules different from our own. In more technical terms, in the sub-atomic world, it is predicted that the more closely one pins down one measure (such as the position of a particle), the less precise another measurement pertaining to the same particle (such as its momentum) must become. (This is known as Heisenberg's uncertainty principle.) Many unexplained anomalies remain. Some interpretations of the sub-atomic world suggest how multiverses hypothetically might come into existence.

SOLAR SYSTEM: The system containing the sun and the bodies held in its gravitational field, including the planets (Mercury, Venus, Earth, Mars, Jupiter, Saturn, Uranus, and Neptune), dwarf planets, moons, asteroids, and comets.

STAR: A celestial body consisting of a mass of gas held together by its own gravity.

THEIST: A person who believes in the existence of God, especially in God as creator, and the ultimate reason why anything exists and functions.

UNIVERSE: All matter and energy, including, the earth, the galaxies, and the contents of intergalactic space, regarded as a whole.

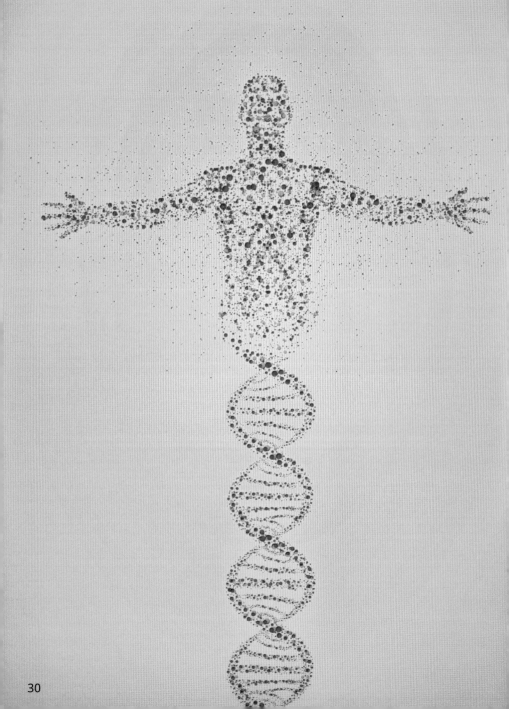

Programme 2 :
EXPLORING THE GOD QUESTION -
LIFE AND EVOLUTION (PART 1)

Programme 1 investigated some of the wonders of the origin and development of the cosmos. Now we focus on a most astonishing characteristic of our universe: life itself.

WHAT IS AT STAKE IN THIS PROGRAMME...

. . . IS WHETHER OR NOT IT IS JUSTIFIABLE TO CLAIM THAT UNGUIDED EVOLUTIONARY FORCES, WITHOUT THE INVOLVEMENT OF A CREATOR ARE, IN THEMSELVES, POWERFUL ENOUGH TO HAVE PRODUCED ALL OF THE SOPHISTICATED LIFE FORMS THAT HAVE EVER EXISTED, INCLUDING HUMAN BEINGS.

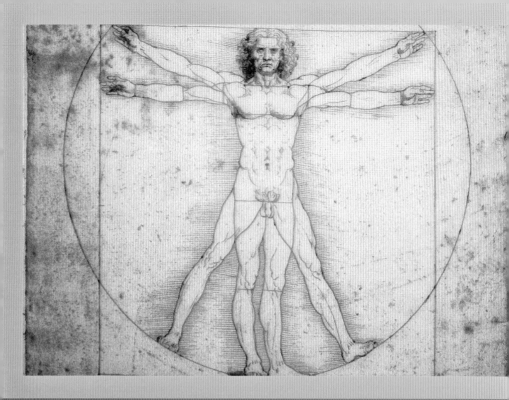

INTRODUCING LIFE AND EVOLUTION

In orthodox science, understanding the development of life is rooted in the work of Charles Darwin and his theory of evolution. Since the publication of Darwin's "On the Origin of Species" in 1859, atheists have seized on Darwin's work in their effort to dispense with God. Consequently, millions across the world live on the assumption that they must choose between evolution and belief in a creator. They include some in the Christian church who see no possible means of reconciling evolution with the Genesis account of creation. The same issue arises in Islam.

BUT EVEN IF EVOLUTION IS EVENTUALLY REJECTED, ON THEOLOGICAL AND/OR SCIENTIFIC GROUNDS, FIRST IT SHOULD BE UNDERSTOOD.

The main intention of this series is to examine if orthodox science – including evolution - leaves space for God.

Part one of the programme explains and illustrates the basic principles that evolutionists believe are operating in the natural world but it also demonstrates that there are well respected eminent evolutionary scientists who are people of faith. They argue that evolution succeeds because it is the work of a creator who wanted it to be so. This suggests that it is not the science that opposes God but rather how atheists interpret it.

Nevertheless, other scientists, many of them within the Christian community, are sceptical about fundamental aspects of Darwinism. Their perspective is also presented.

Some objections to evolution are more theological than scientific. In that regard, Part 2 includes some debate about the interpretation of the opening chapters of Genesis.

The ongoing debate about our origins, evolution, the Bible and God is fundamentally important. This programme aims to help viewers to understand it better and to identify for themselves where they stand on these highly significant issues.

Regardless of which scientific theories most accurately describe the development of life on earth, arguably the most important question is whether its very success seems ultimately to be the work of a creator or the product of chance and good fortune.

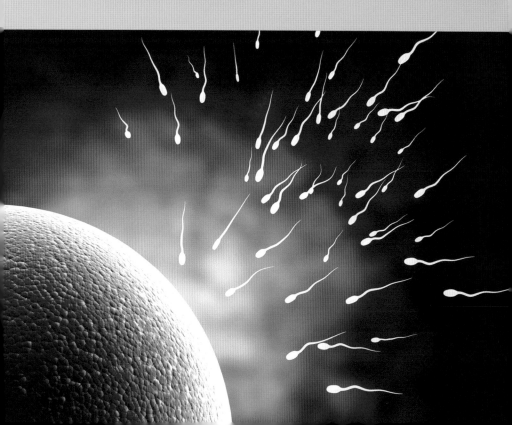

PROGRAMME 2 PART 1 : CONTENT GUIDE

The following guide to content is to help you to follow the narrative of the programme as easily as possible. Each coloured dot also appears on the screen to provide you with a cross reference. Please note that the duration of Programme 2 Part 1 (40 minutes) is longer than other parts of the series. After 25 minutes, a fade to black indicates an opportunity to pause the programme to reflect on the story so far. This occurs at the end of dot 8 below. Any of questions 1,2,3,5 and 7 could be discussed at this stage.

1 Setting the scene.

2 Clearly, life itself is the most wonderful phenomenon - prompting the question: where did it all come from?

3 The most widely accepted explanation for the development of life is evolution. It has become a key issue in the science/religion debate, with Darwinism often being promoted as an alternative to a creator.

4 Many believers reject evolution. However, some high profile scientists are Christians *and* committed Darwinian Evolutionists.

5 Whether evolution is accepted or rejected, it should at least be understood.

- Darwin's journey to fame began when, as ship's naturalist on the Beagle, he embarked on a round-the-world voyage.

- He observed that, across the world, creatures develop variations, some of which become crucial to survival. Those which survive appear to have been 'selected' by nature. He called this 'natural selection.'

- Darwin speculated that, over vast periods of time, an accumulation of small changes has produced the variety of species we find in all of life on earth.

6 In terms of 19th Century reaction to Darwin's theory of evolution by natural selection:

- The Church appeared to embrace it.

- The Church's opponents seized on it.

7 Fossils are an important source of evidence for the astonishing evolutionary development of life on earth.

8 Atheists argue that Darwin has replaced any need for God but theists challenge the view that evolution takes God out of the picture.

9 Not all scientists are convinced by the explanatory power of evolution. Advocates of Intelligent Design argue that natural selection is not a sufficient explanation. They claim that the natural world reveals specific evidence of a designer's mind at work.

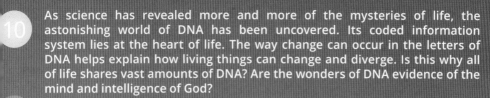

10 As science has revealed more and more of the mysteries of life, the astonishing world of DNA has been uncovered. Its coded information system lies at the heart of life. The way change can occur in the letters of DNA helps explain how living things can change and diverge. Is this why all of life shares vast amounts of DNA? Are the wonders of DNA evidence of the mind and intelligence of God?

11 Is atheism or theism the better explanation?

PLAY

VIEW PROGRAMME

THE BIG ISSUES

? WHY DOES **EVOLUTION** APPARENTLY POSE SUCH A **THREAT TO GOD?**

? BELIEF IN THE POWER OF **NATURAL SELECTION** LIES AT THE HEART OF **DARWINIAN EVOLUTION.** HOW PERSUADED ARE YOU BY DARWIN'S CENTRAL IDEA?

? RICHARD DAWKINS BELIEVES THERE IS THE **"APPEARANCE OF DESIGN"** IN NATURE. WHAT DO YOU THINK HE MEANS BY 'DESIGN' AND HOW DO YOU RESPOND TO HIS ARGUMENT THAT **BLIND FORCES OF EVOLUTION** CONVINCINGLY EXPLAIN THE "APPEARANCE OF DESIGN"?

? HOW RELEVANT TO THE GOD QUESTION IS THE EXISTENCE OF THE **DNA INFORMATION** THAT IS NOW KNOWN TO BE **CRUCIAL** IN THE CONSTRUCTION OF **ALL LIVING CELLS?**

Programme 2 :

EXPLORING THE GOD QUESTION - LIFE AND EVOLUTION (PART 1)

FOR MORE IN-DEPTH DISCUSSION

RESPONDING TO EVOLUTION

"People are responding to code words (evolution and creation)."

Paul Froese

Paul Froese seems to be suggesting that people have a tendency to adopt views on this subject which are based on feelings and intuition more than on knowledge.

Do you think he is right?

If so, what are the dangers of developing beliefs in this way?

WHAT ROLE FOR A CREATOR

"The very conception of God has been muscled off the scientific playing field."

David Sloan Wilson

"This is basically science teaching us something about God's creative plan."

Francis Collins

Why is evolution so important to atheists?

If life evolved more or less in the way Darwin described, which of the following do you think are true and why?

• There is no need for a creator

• There is still a compelling argument for a creator

• There is less need for a creator

QUESTION 1   QUESTION 2

UNDERSTANDING NATURAL SELECTION

"In many ways, Darwin's theory has the aura of common sense."

Carol Cleland

Do you agree with Carol Cleland that 'natural selection' has the "aura of common sense"?

What do you think it explains?

CHALLENGING THE EXPLANATORY POWER OF NATURAL SELECTION

"What is the evidence of natural selection? Finch beaks changing size. Very small scale evolutionary changes. That's the only direct evidence we have for the power of natural selection."

William Dembski

"Natural Selection is well proven but natural selection is not an engine for changing creatures one to the other."

Andy McIntosh

"Can it explain new organs, new body parts?...It's possible but there's a lot of reasons to doubt it".

Stephen Meyer

An obstacle to discussing evolution is that relatively few people might understand it well enough to reach informed conclusions. Nevertheless, what reactions do you have to the doubts expressed in the above statements?

Do you think the question of God's existence is linked in any way to evolution by natural selection being substantially true or false?

QUESTION 3   QUESTION 4

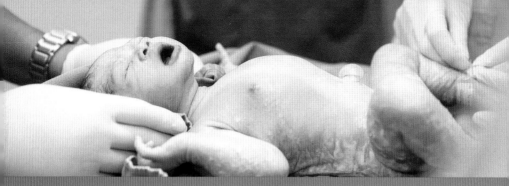

CONSIDERING COMMON ANCESTRY

"He (Darwin) reached another dramatic conclusion: that all of life's diverse forms – including human beings – could have evolved step by step from one original cell."

Narrator

Darwin could not rely on direct evidence to substantiate his theory of common origin. With the little direct evidence that Darwin had, do you think he came to a reasonable conclusion?

Do you think 'the God question' is affected by whether or not life on earth evolved from a common ancestor?

LOOKING AT THE EVIDENCE FOR COMMON ANCESTRY

"All of life on earth, from the simplest bacterium...to a mushroom, to a human being is remarkably similar at the molecular (DNA) level."

Carol Cleland

"It looks as if the further back in time we go, the smaller and simpler the organisms get."

Martin Brasier

As evidence for common ancestry, do you think these facts provide:

• convincing evidence

• quite strong evidence

• rather weak evidence?

QUESTION 5   QUESTION 6

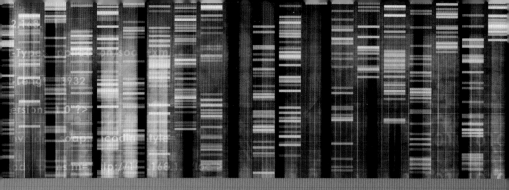

REACTIONS OF THE CHURCH

"The leadership of the Anglican Church...mostly accepted the idea."

Michael Reiss

"Darwin's a false friend to these people (the church)."

Steve Fuller

"Darwin...by and large wanted to stay on the sidelines with respect to these things."

Michael Ruse

What do you think is the predominant reaction of the church today to evolution?

Is it relevant and important for the church to be concerned with the question 'Is faith in a creator compatible with evolutionary theory?' Or should the church 'stay on the sidelines with respect to these things'?

FAITH IN EVOLUTION

"I sometimes think of it (evolution) as a factory for making almost impossible things."

Steve Jones

"The errors might lead to you and me."

Peter Atkins

"This is basically science teaching us something about what was really happening with God's creative plan."

Francis Collins

How much do you think the theist and the atheist positions each require faith?

QUESTION 7   QUESTION 8

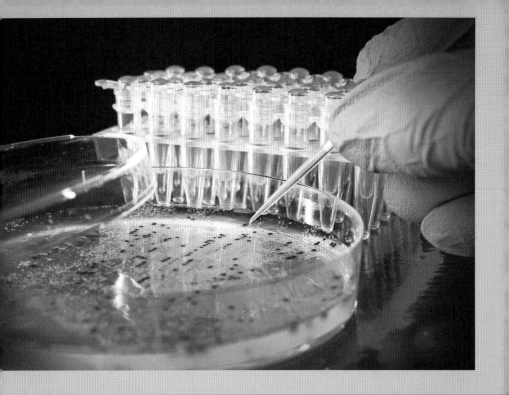

Programme 2:
EXPLORING THE GOD QUESTION - LIFE AND EVOLUTION (PART 2)

WHAT IS AT STAKE IN THIS PROGRAMME...

....IS WHETHER OR NOT IT IS JUSTIFIABLE TO CLAIM THAT UNGUIDED EVOLUTIONARY FORCES, WITHOUT ANY INVOLVEMENT OF A CREATOR ARE, IN THEMSELVES, POWERFUL ENOUGH TO HAVE PRODUCED ALL THE SOPHISTICATED LIFE FORMS THAT HAVE EVER EXISTED INCLUDING HUMAN BEINGS.

SPECIFICALLY IN PART 2...

How convincing is the evolutionary account and can it really be compatible with belief in God and reverence for Holy Scripture?

PROGRAMME 2 PART 2 : CONTENT GUIDE

This content guide is to help you follow the narrative of the programme as easily as possible. Each coloured dot appears on the screen to provide you with a cross reference.

1 A reminder of key points raised in Part 1.

2 As scientists have tried to understand the development of life, three significantly different viewpoints have emerged: atheism, theistic evolution and intelligent design.

3 At the heart of the evolutionary explanation lies a key question: Can a system that appears to operate randomly really explain the development of life?

4 Evolution has attempted to explain the diversity of life but, meanwhile, life's origin remains a mystery.

5 Life itself has developed within the special conditions offered by planet earth. This is not something that Darwinian evolution can explain.

6 For those who believe in evolution and God, there are some significant challenges to face. Principally:

- Could the cruelty evident in the natural world be part of a creator's plan?

- Could a system which is essentially chance-based be relied upon to produce creatures 'in the image of God'?

- How can the Genesis creation story be reconciled with the evolutionary story?

7 Despite the apparent contrasts between the two, a leading scientist has discovered mysterious connections between the Genesis and the evolutionary accounts.

8 Reaching a conclusion on the 'God and evolution' DEBATE.

VIEW PROGRAMME

PLAY

THE BIG ISSUES

EVOLUTION DEPENDS ON **'RANDOM' CHANGES** TAKING PLACE IN **ORGANISMS**. SOME ARGUE THAT, GIVEN ENOUGH TIME, THIS IS A VIABLE WAY FOR SOPHISTICATED **LIFE TO DEVELOP**; OTHERS DISPUTE THAT.
WHAT DO YOU THINK?

DO YOU THINK THERE CAN BE ANY ACCOMMODATION BETWEEN **GENESIS 1 AND 2** AND **EVOLUTIONARY BIOLOGY?**

THE PROGRAMME RAISES SOME IMPORTANT ISSUES THAT NEED TO BE RESOLVED IF ONE WISHES TO BE A **DARWINIAN** AND A **BELIEVER IN GOD**.
THESE INCLUDE:

- WHETHER OR NOT THE SUFFERING WHICH IS APPARENTLY AN INTEGRAL PART OF THE EVOLUTIONARY PROCESS IS COMPATIBLE WITH A GOOD AND LOVING GOD;

- HOW A RANDOM 'CHANCE' PROCESS COULD BE RELIED UPON TO PRODUCE CREATURES IN THE IMAGE OF GOD.

(MORE DETAILS ARE GIVEN IN APPENDIX 3.)

DO YOU THINK THESE ISSUES ARE RESOLVABLE OR IS EVOLUTION NOT CONSISTENT WITH BELIEF IN A CREATOR?

43

Programme 2 :

EXPLORING THE GOD QUESTION - LIFE AND EVOLUTION (PART 2)

FOR MORE IN-DEPTH DISCUSSION

THEISTIC EVOLUTION

"I am a theist and I'm also an evolutionist because I think ultimately the evolutionary process exists in....God's providential plan."

Ken Miller

"It (evolution) is in no way subverting the idea of creation we have in Genesis 1 to 3. It's simply...answering the question 'how did God do it?' "

Denis Alexander

How much do you agree with the above?

For a summary of *Four Distinct Perspectives on Evolution*, see Appendix 1

QUESTION 1

NOTE ON QUESTION 2

All are agreed that the evolutionary explanation depends on a large element of chance based on trial and error processes. Some find this an unconvincing explanation for the diversity and sophistication of life on earth while others accept it as entirely credible, given the enormous period of time involved.

Atheists argue that the blind trial and error forces of evolution have produced millions of species which have triumphed while many more have been eliminated. No God.

Theistic evolutionists adopt the same scientific explanation but argue that God is behind the process and has ensured its success from the start.

Intelligent Design advocates are more sceptical about the evolutionary explanation and see instead the direct involvement of a creator at key stages in the development of life.

TRIAL AND ERROR

"The things that have to go right are so incredibly improbable that it's really not a plausible explanation to rely on natural selection and random mutation to produce the big changes."

Stephen Meyer

"One in a trillion, trillion, trillion, trillion, trillion, trillion or so sequences that are possible would (be needed to) perform a specified function."

Doug Axe

"What is so difficult...is to really imagine the opportunity from three and a half thousand million years for natural selection and the other pressures on evolution to work."

Michael Reiss

Some argue the evolutionary explanation is too improbable; others claim it just needs enough time. Which argument are you inclined to believe?

THE ORIGIN OF LIFE

"We really don't have the evidence we need to have a very compelling scientific story about how life originated on earth."

Carol Cleland

"...And without that to start the ball rolling, Darwin's theory is fundamentally incomplete."

William Dembski

Supposing science had a convincing explanation for how life began, would this affect the argument for the existence of God?

QUESTION 2   QUESTION 3

INTELLIGENT DESIGN?

"When we find information in the cell (the language of DNA), this is not something that Darwinian evolution.... can explain. But we do have an explanation that is known to produce information and that explanation is intelligence: conscious activity."

Stephen Meyer

"It has to have accumulated by pre-cellular evolution by natural selection."

Daniel Dennett

"The moment we see text with meaning – and it's a code remember – we infer upwards to intelligence instantly."

John Lennox

How convinced are you that only intelligence can produce 'information'?

What difference would it make to your answer if one day the development of information is able to be scientifically understood as part of a natural process?

GOD AND/OR DARWIN?

"One can be a Christian and a committed Darwinian evolutionist... and I've never seen any conflict between the two."

Denis Alexander

"Can you be a Darwinian and a Christian? Yes, but it's not easy."

Michael Ruse

Do you agree or disagree with Michael Ruse's answer to his own question? What are some of the points of potential conflict?

Can they be resolved?

See Appendix 3 / *Issues for Theistic Evolutionists*

QUESTION 4   QUESTION 5

GENESIS AND ORTHODOX SCIENCE

Believers are likely to accept that the first two chapters of Genesis communicate a message about the existence of God and his plan to create a world in which there are creatures which can have a relationship with him.

However, there is controversy about a literal interpretation of six twenty-four hour days. The argument that the world was created in six days conflicts directly with the conclusions of contemporary science and is one of the reasons why science and religion are sometimes thought to be incompatible.

Andrew Parker, however, suggests that there is a compatibility that few have thought about before - a chronological sequence in the creation story which matches remarkably well with the evolutionary story.

"One of the mistakes that people make is to read Genesis 1 and 2 as if it was a scientific account of six days of hectic divine activity."

John Polkinghorne

"The days have to be regarded in an ordinary sense as twenty-four hour days."

Andy McIntosh

"The Bible doesn't insist that the earth is young."

John Lennox

"The writer of Genesis has the whole (evolutionary) sequence in the right order......I'm starting to find space for God."

Andrew Parker

Is it important to interpret the days of Genesis as periods of 24 hours? Why? Why not?"

Do you find any significance in Andrew Parker's observation and conclusion?

To what extent should the findings of orthodox science be taken into account when interpreting the meaning of the opening chapters of Genesis?

QUESTION 6

INTERPRETING THE EVIDENCE

"I would accuse God of playing a malicious trick in providing all the evidence that he didn't exist."

Daniel Dennett

"There are a lot of things that make strong atheism the least rational of all the choices."

Francis Collins

"Evolution without God is too good to be true."

Michael Reiss

Does evolution leave space for - or even need – God?

For a summary of *The Case for Theism / The Case for Atheism*, see Appendix 2.

AND FINALLY...

"You cannot use evolution to account for its own existence."

John Lennox

"You cannot deduce atheism from Darwinism."

John Lennox

Do you agree?

QUESTION 7

QUESTION 8

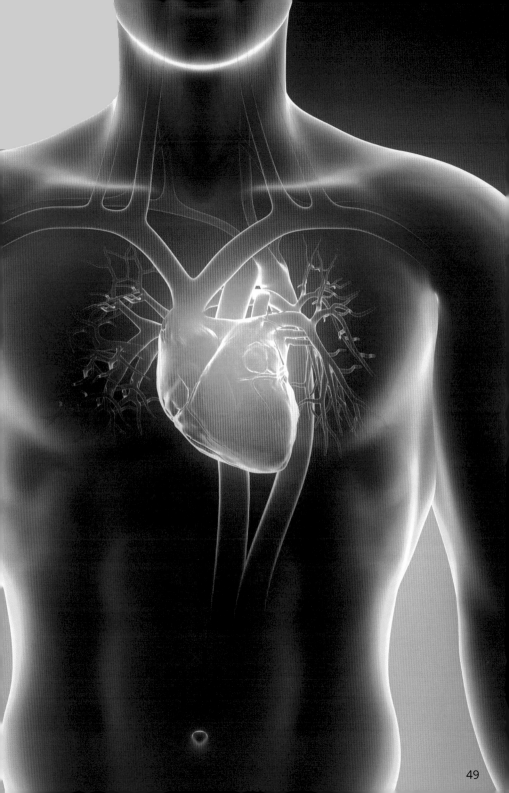

APPENDIX 1: FOUR DISTINCT PERSPECTIVES ON EVOLUTION

Introduction

Increasingly, since the publication of Darwin's "On the Origin of Species" in 1859, evolution has become the dominating idea in life sciences. Atheists present evolution as the scientific alternative to God. However, many theists (highly prominent scientists among them) embrace evolution - seeing it as God's method of creation - and object to it being offered as an alternative to God. Other theists have different levels of difficulty with evolution and some reject it altogether.

Atheistic Evolution

Atheists argue that, over billions of years - and with no need for a creator at any stage - the blind forces of natural selection have produced all the variety of species that have ever existed. Sophisticated human beings also emerged from that process. The origin of all life is derived from the first living cell. However most admit that it is not yet known how life began. God is unnecessary because the whole process is capable of developing by itself.

Theistic Evolution

Theistic evolutionists agree with the orthodox scientific explanation for the development of life. That is, natural forces are sufficient to create all the diversity and sophistication that we see but that this has resulted from the potential built into the universe by God at the first moments of creation. Theistic evolutionists generally take the view that God sustains the laws of the universe and holds the whole system in place. For them, evolution by natural selection operates within that broad framework and is largely responsible for all the diversity and sophistication in the natural world. Through evolution, God has given nature freedom with potential. All evolutionists accept that the processes took place over vast periods of time, estimated to be around four billion years of time on earth.

Intelligent Design

Intelligent Design proponents hold that certain identifiable features of the natural world and of living things are best explained by an intelligent cause rather than an undirected process such as natural selection. There are many immensely complex biological phenomena that are too sophisticated to have evolved through a series of chance mutations. The complexities of just one single living cell is a prime example. The wonder of the human genome built by the language of DNA is another. This information is like an instruction book for how every living thing is constructed. The inference is that this is scientific evidence of a designing mind at work. Some intelligent design proponents accept that evolutionary forces operate in the world but that they are far from being the whole story.

Young Earth Creationism

Whereas most scientists believe the world is more than 4 billion years old, Young Earth Creationists claim that the earth is of much more recent origin (usually less than 10,000 years) and that God created the universe, the world and all original life forms including human beings in six twenty-four hour days. This view is rooted in the belief that the early chapters of Genesis in the Bible must be interpreted literally. Such timescales are far too short for evolution to work. The implication therefore is that evolutionary scientists are mistaken in their interpretation of the evidence.

APPENDIX 2: THE CASE FOR THEISM / THE CASE FOR ATHEISM

IN SUMMARY, THE CONCLUSION OF CONTEMPORARY SCIENCE is that the earth is very old – about 4.7 billion years. It is believed that about one billion years after earth's formation, somehow, a series of chemical processes combined to provide the initial spark of life.

For millions of years, life forms were very simple but, over time, by the processes of natural selection, organisms became more complex. Through the ages, a huge accumulation of small changes led to increasing differences between organisms which, in turn, resulted in the emergence of entirely new species. It is believed human beings developed through this evolutionary process.

The fossil record seems to support the view that organisms became more complex over time. Some scientists claim to have discovered fossils which appear to capture species in transition. Acanthostega is one example. Further, evolutionary science argues that, since all living things share remarkable similarities in their DNA, this is also evidence for common ancestry.

For these reasons, evolution by natural selection is believed by most scientists to be the best and most comprehensive scientific explanation of the development of diverse life on earth.

IN SUMMARY,
THE CASE FOR THEISM is made in at least three different ways. Theistic Evolutionists accept Darwinian evolution as a scientific explanation but see evidence that God is behind it. For them, the grandeur and wonder of life demands an explanation that goes beyond understanding scientific processes alone.

The natural world functions in a highly complex way and while science is able to reveal something of how those processes work – for example through evolution - the whole system is too wonderful and looks too purposeful for it to have been generated entirely by chance. The big picture strongly suggests an overarching mind.

Intelligent Design advocates, while accepting some aspects of evolution, maintain that specific characteristics of the natural world appear to have no other explanation than that they were designed. They argue that, under scrutiny, evolutionary theory is unable to explain convincingly how random changes can offer natural selection the choices it needs to operate successfully. The discovery that information lies at the heart of life's processes in every living cell convinces them further of a creator's mind at work.

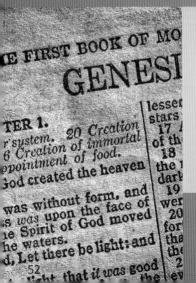

Young Earth Creationists reject Darwinian evolution. It requires a timescale which they believe is not supported by the Genesis account of creation. Orthodox dating systems are deemed unreliable or inaccurate in their interpretation of the scientific evidence. The possibility that human beings emerged from the evolutionary process is believed to be at loggerheads with scripture.

All theists believe that the emergence of creatures with intelligence and spiritual awareness was God's intention.

IN SUMMARY,
THE CASE FOR ATHEISM is that, especially since Darwin, God is not necessary as an explanation. Admittedly, nature looks designed but Darwin has explained how natural processes can create the appearance of design. The key is natural selection. This is a self perpetuating process leading to development and change and does not require a god to interfere or specially create anything. This process of natural selection has operated since life first began. Scientific evidence (the fossil record and the vast amounts of DNA shared among species) points to life diversifying from a common original source. Once life has begun, evolution takes over and is capable of producing all the diversity and sophistication we see in the natural world today.

Human beings are simply part of a purposeless process and have no special place.

LINKED TO QUESTION 5: ISSUES FOR THEISTIC EVOLUTIONISTS

SUFFERING

Surely there is a better creation method than one involving so much pain and suffering!

"God works through evolution. If that turns out to be true, then it's one more piece of evidence for God being malign because the mechanism of evolution is so cruel."

Peter Atkins

"In order for the natural world to be really free and allow for freewill in humans we had to allow for this kind of suffering to take place."

Celia Deane-Drummond

HUMAN BEINGS

Surely the randomness of evolution could not be relied upon to produce creatures that are sophisticated and intelligent and could even be God conscious!

"Absolutely central to Christian belief is that we humans are made in the image of God: that at some level we had to be."

Michael Ruse

"There is absolutely no evidence of any kind of forethought..or plan..in evolution."

Steve Jones

"Evolution does end up with organisms that are intelligent...If you re-ran the tape of life...you'd probably end up with creatures – even if they looked rather different to us - having discussions about the nature of an Almighty."

Michael Reiss

ISSUE 1

ISSUE 2

MADE IN THE IMAGE OF GOD

Where in the evolutionary process came the ability to be God conscious and be spiritual creatures?

"One way of understanding what's going on is that God did choose some... farmers, maybe Adam and Eve of the Genesis account whom he brought into fellowship with himself."

Denis Alexander

"God literally took the ground and out of it made Adam."

Andy McIntosh

DEATH AND 'THE FALL'

If – according to Christian theology – death entered the world as the result of the sin of Adam and Eve, how could there have been an earlier evolutionary process with so much death before Adam and Eve even existed?

"It all really hinges on no death before the fall."

Andy McIntosh

"We find Adam and Eve disobeying God...but they didn't drop dead. We read of this amazing account of them being cast out of the garden of Eden; a most vivid picture of *spiritual* death."

Denis Alexander

ISSUE 3   ISSUE 4

APPENDIX 4: UNDERSTANDING THE TERMS

Although every attempt is made to keep scientific explanations as simple as possible, the use of some technical, or less familiar, terms is inevitable.

AGNOSTIC: A person, having no active belief in God, uncertain whether or not God exists, and perhaps even believing the truth about God's existence cannot be known.

ATHEIST: A person who explicitly denies the existence of any gods.

CAMBRIAN EXPLOSION: A period of time calculated to be around 540 million years ago when there appears to have been an explosion in the development and diversity of species. It is sometimes known as the big bang of evolution.

DARWINIAN EVOLUTION: The theory proposed by Charles Darwin that all species have come from a single life form in a process analogous to a tree deriving from a single seed and then spreading its life to its branches. Natural selection is responsible for those species that survive and for those that become extinct.

DEEP TIME: A period 3.4 billion years ago when it appears that all life forms were very simple.

DNA: Coded information at the heart of living cells. This information provides the instructions for how the organism is built.

EVOLUTION: The process through which life forms change and develop. The word is used in a variety of ways. It can simply refer to the fact of change or be used in a more scientific context to describe the way in which a life form changes or adapts. Such changes might be very small and subtle or they could be more extensive. In a more comprehensive sense, evolution refers to the development and diversity of all life from a single source.

GENE: A unit of DNA providing instructions for a specific aspect of an organism.

GENETICS: The science of the study of genes.

GENOME: The full DNA instruction book for a whole creature, eg a human being.

NATURAL SELECTION: The name given to the process through which creatures randomly develop assets that become helpful or even crucial to their survival – sometimes at the expense of other species which are not so well adapted to their environment.

NEO DARWINISM: Contemporary forms of Darwinian evolution informed by the benefit of subsequent research and discovery.

RANDOM MUTATION: Changes which occur without obvious explanation in the DNA instructions of any creature. Because these changes sometimes occur during reproduction, they are sometimes referred to as "copying mistakes" or "errors".

THEIST: A person who believes in the existence of God, especially in God as creator and the ultimate reason why anything exists and functions.

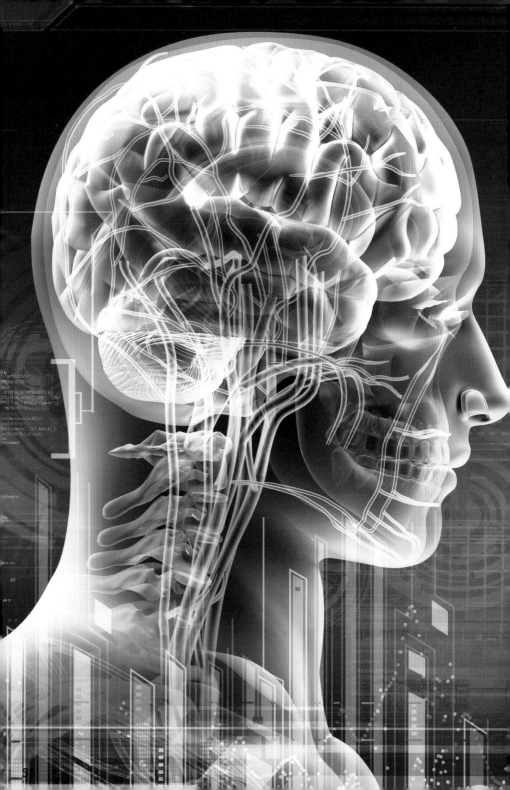

Programme 3 :
EXPLORING THE GOD QUESTION -
MIND AND CONSCIOUSNESS (PART 1)

WHAT IS AT STAKE IN THIS PROGRAMME...

...IS WHETHER THE EXISTENCE OF HUMAN CONSCIOUSNESS – INCLUDING SPIRITUAL AND MORAL CONSCIOUSNESS – POINTS TO A MIND BEHIND THE UNIVERSE.

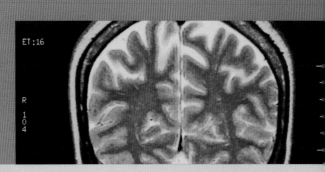

In the first programme, we probed some of the mysteries of our universe including the significance of finely balanced forces that permit life to exist. We debated whether such sophistication might be just 'luck' or, instead, points to an organising mind behind the universe.

In the second programme, we investigated the sheer wonder of life on earth and explored – and critiqued - the insights offered by Charles Darwin about the processes that have created life's glorious diversity. We learned how the science of genetics has revealed the astonishing and creative mechanisms that sustain and reproduce life forms and queried if blind chance or a creator's intention appears the more likely explanation.

INTRODUCING MIND & CONSCIOUSNESS

In programme three, we focus on the wonders of the human mind and brain. We ask if their awesome power to make us conscious, to allow us to think, to create and to reach out for ultimate explanations might be the product of natural processes alone; or, instead, provide the means through which we can discover, and relate to, the creator.

PROGRAMME 3 PART 1 : CONTENT GUIDE

This content guide is to help you follow the narrative of the programme as easily as possible. Each coloured dot appears on the screen to provide you with a cross reference.

1. Setting the scene.

2. Human consciousness is an extraordinary phenomenon. It includes awareness of ourselves and the world around but also extends to higher levels of consciousness and even God consciousness.

3. Consciousness is linked to the human brain; itself a source of wonder.

4. Significantly, the mind can be distinguished from the brain.

5. The existence of higher levels of consciousness prompt the question: are we essentially spiritual creatures?

6. Trying to explain consciousness is one of the greatest challenges to science. Inevitably, there are attempts to find answers in evolution.

7. Some argue that consciousness may be a separate entity from the brain. If so, it might support the view that our 'spiritual selves' are in some ways separate from our physical selves.

8. A sense of spirituality, especially expressed in religious practices, is widespread across the world. Ely Cathedral is a prime example of how designers and craftsmen have expressed their 'God-consciousness' in architecture. Do such buildings represent an actual spiritual reality?

9. Human beings have a natural tendency to believe so it is important to question why we believe what we believe.

60

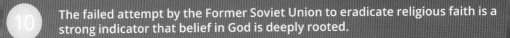

10   The failed attempt by the Former Soviet Union to eradicate religious faith is a strong indicator that belief in God is deeply rooted.

11   Across the world, religious traditions vary widely. So is belief merely cultural? Can truth be determined?

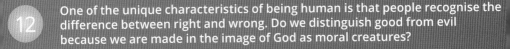

12   One of the unique characteristics of being human is that people recognise the difference between right and wrong. Do we distinguish good from evil because we are made in the image of God as moral creatures?

▶ PLAY   VIEW PROGRAMME

THE BIG ISSUES

?   DOES THE **MYSTERY** AND THE **POWER** OF **HUMAN CONSCIOUSNESS** CONTRIBUTE MEANINGFULLY TO THE DEBATE ABOUT **GOD'S EXISTENCE?**

?   DOES THE WIDESPREAD POPULARITY OF **RELIGION** OFFER **EVIDENCE** THAT THERE IS A **SUPERNATURAL REALITY** OR IS THIS MORE A SIGN OF HUMAN **WISHFUL THINKING**, A **SUPERSTITIOUS PAST** AND EXPRESSIONS OF **VULNERABILITY?**

?   CAN HUMAN BEINGS BE 'GOOD' WITHOUT GOD?

Programme 3 :

EXPLORING THE GOD QUESTION - MIND AND CONSCIOUSNESS (PART 1

FOR MORE IN-DEPTH DISCUSSION

THE BRAIN, MIND AND CONSCIOUSNESS

"The greatest, the most awesome phenomenon in the universe: the human brain."

Narrator

"I think the biggest mystery of consciousness is how it comes to be."

Sam Parnia

"I like to think of the mind as the conscious part of the brain."

Chris Frith

NOTE ON QUESTION 2

Some contributors to the programme (including composer John Rutter and Rev Canon Dr Alan Hargrave) talk of experiences that seem to connect us with something outside of ourselves. This might be, for example, listening to an extraordinarily powerful piece of music or experiencing the grandeur of a cathedral.

What are some of the things you find impressive about the human brain?

How surprising is it that so little is understood by science about why we are conscious beings – aware of ourselves, others and past experience?

Does the complexity, mystery and power of the brain and mind seem to you to be relevant evidence in discussing the God question?

QUESTION 1

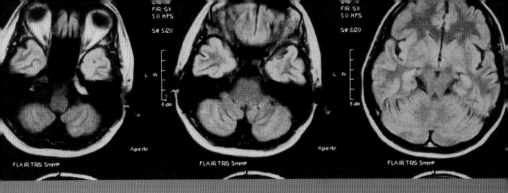

THE BRAIN AND SPIRITUAL EXPERIENCE

"It seems to me that music has some mysterious core which is probably spiritual."

John Rutter

"There is a sense of God's grace and presence and a sense of being loved which is a profound and meaningful experience."

Alan Hargrave

What do these contributors seem to be saying about the remarkable scope of human consciousness?

Does this in any way connect with your own experience?

Is God the explanation?

BELIEFS AND BELIEVING

"People are disappointingly gullible in their belief systems."

Justin Barrett

"The brain is really a belief machine. It has no choice but to construct beliefs about everything."

Andrew Newberg

"Religious beliefs maybe need that extra scrutiny."

Justin Barrett

How much of a tendency do we have to "swallow" more or less unquestioningly what we've been taught by our families, peers and our culture?

Do you think religion could be just another form of gullibility or superstition?

What are the dangers of being unquestioning? How can we try to ensure our beliefs are truly selected by us rather than simply given to us?

QUESTION 2   QUESTION 3

faith

RELIGION AND CULTURE

THE SEARCH FOR TRUTH

"One of the roots of belief is cultural conditioning."

Peter Atkins

"It doesn't follow from that that there isn't some kind of natural anchor that tethers all of these different beliefs."

Justin Barrett

"The primary concern of religions is to have a sense of union...with a supreme reality. That is common to all major world traditions."

Keith Ward

Different religions flourish in separate parts of the world. Do you think this provides clear evidence that religions are merely products of their cultures? Or, on the contrary, do you think it indicates that, around the world, people have a natural sense of a spiritual reality?

If Keith Ward (above) is right, what significance do you find in that fact?

"Truth claims are not equally valid or equally valuable."

Stuart McAllister

"The Christian faith claims to be the truth about salvation. God became flesh, revealed himself to us through his son and we can know this God."

Stuart McAllister

"My God is revealed in scripture and primarily in Jesus Christ. It's open for everybody to see exactly what kind of God that is and there is the possibility of having a relationship with him."

John Lennox

How do you think we can recognise truth in religious claims? What would count as evidence?

How do you respond to the statements above? Do you believe they are true? Why? Why not?

QUESTION 4

QUESTION 5

THE SENSE OF RIGHT AND WRONG

THE BIG QUESTION

"Everybody can behave morally... because everyone's made in the image of God as a moral being."

John Lennox

"We can elevate our moral systems using the engine that evolution gave us consisting of our reasoning faculties."

Steven Pinker

"If there is an immaterial mind in each human being, there probably is an immaterial mind behind the universe."

Denyse O'Leary

"It may be that the human mind interacts with the brain...but it isn't produced from the brain."

Sam Parnia

Human beings possess a moral sense. How relevant is this to the God question?

In the programme, there are two opposing points of view about the origin of the human mind and consciousness. One is that they have evolved as a function of the human brain; the other is that the mind might have a separate existence and uses the brain as a way of connecting with our physical selves.

Do you think it matters? Why?

QUESTION 6   QUESTION 7

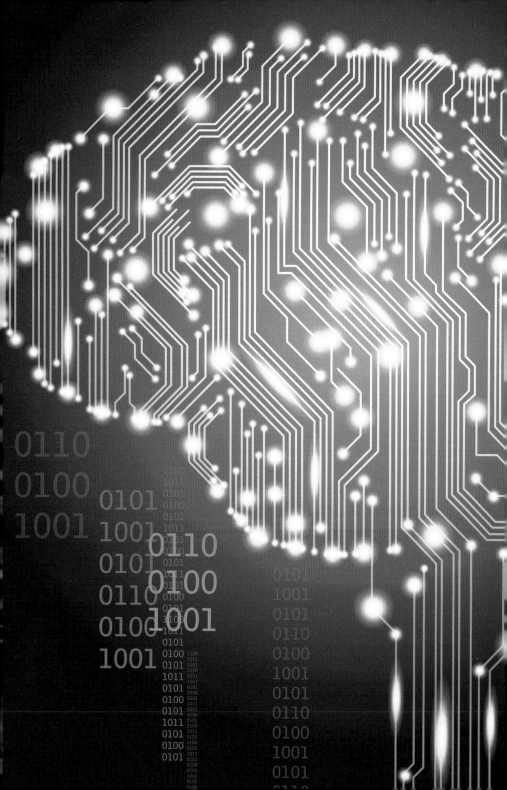

Programme 3:
EXPLORING THE GOD QUESTION - MIND AND CONSCIOUSNESS (PART 2)

WHAT IS AT STAKE IN THIS PROGRAMME...

...IS WHETHER THE EXISTENCE OF HUMAN CONSCIOUSNESS - INCLUDING SPIRITUAL AND MORAL CONSCIOUSNESS - POINTS TO A MIND BEHIND THE UNIVERSE.

SPECIFICALLY IN PART 2...

Is there reliable and valid evidence in human experience that points to spiritual reality and the existence of God?

PROGRAMME 3 PART 2 : CONTENT GUIDE

This content guide is to help you follow the narrative of the programme as easily as possible. Each coloured dot appears on the screen to provide you with a cross reference.

1. A reminder of key points raised in Part 1.

2. Some believers claim a clear sense of God in their lives. A leader in a seminary attempts to explain his 'God consciousness'.

3. A scientific study in the USA has suggested a 'sense of God' could just be the action of a 'god spot' in the human brain. Others argue that this thesis is unsustainable.

4. Central to the theist argument is the belief that human existence does not cease at the point of death. A scientific investigation has been studying evidence for consciousness beyond clinical brain death. Accident victim, Don Piper, recounts his own Near Death Experience.

5. In pointing to evidence for the existence of God, some believers highlight the significance of personal experience in their own transformed lives and argue that, to them, this is clear evidence for the existence of God.

6. Decision time: does consciousness provide important evidence for the existence of God or is it more likely to be the product of natural forces alone?

 **VIEW PROGRAMME**

PLAY

THE BIG ISSUES

? WHAT **CREDIBILITY** CAN BE GIVEN TO ACCOUNTS ABOUT **PERSONAL EXPERIENCE OF GOD?** WHICH ASPECTS OF THE TESTIMONIES GIVEN IN THE PROGRAMME SEEM **BELIEVABLE/LESS BELIEVABLE?**

? HAVE **NEAR DEATH EXPERIENCES** ANY RELEVANCE TO THE GOD QUESTION?

? WHAT LIGHT CAN **SCIENCE** SHED ON CLAIMS OF **SPIRITUAL EXPERIENCE/SPIRITUAL REALITY?** WILL **SCIENCE** EVER BE ABLE TO **PROVIDE ALL THE ANSWERS?**

? SHOULD **GOD GET THE CREDIT** FOR THE **TRANFORMED LIVES** OF BELIEVERS?

Programme 3 :

EXPLORING THE GOD QUESTION - MIND AND CONSCIOUSNESS (PART 2

FOR MORE IN-DEPTH DISCUSSION

SENSING GOD

"We have an experience of something beyond ourselves and very often that experience . . . happens in the context of meditative prayer."

Matthew Green

"God is a lie and people should not waste their time on it."

Peter Atkins

"God is a living person who spiritually speaks to the heart of every person if we'll simply be open to listen to his voice."

William Lane Craig

How do you react to Matthew Green's account of the priests having experience of something beyond themselves? How significant is the "context of meditative prayer"?

Is it credible in the age of science to claim experience of God, given that he cannot be seen or scientifically tested?

PERSONAL TRANSFORMATION

"I had an encounter with God and my life was changed."

Silvia Glover

"I'm no longer rebellious against the things that are morally just and right."

Darryl, Darrington Prisoner

"Christianity . . . produces the results it promises to produce. That's a test of truth."

Chuck Colson

"Religion becomes a confuser .. . it gives people the illusion that there are simple answers to very complicated questions – which there aren't."

Daniel Dennett

Who of the above do you think is convincing and why?

QUESTION 1   QUESTION 2

BELIEVING AND KNOWING

"According to the New Testament there is such a thing as the internal testimony of the Holy Spirit. This is a process that produces knowledge just as much as perception."

Alvin Plantinga

"Science is very important but it is restricted to one sort of reality: namely a sort of reality that everybody can observe."

Keith Ward

"We have to look at all the perspectives that exist and that does include psychological, consciousness, spiritual . . . That may ultimately be as valuable, if not more valuable, than what science may be able to offer."

Andrew Newberg

Is Alvin Plantinga's claim credible or is science the only reliable way to test reality?

What point is Andrew Newberg making? What is the implication for how we might 'know' something to be real or true?

NEAR DEATH EXPERIENCE

"If the brain isn't working but people can gather information, then it's absolutely fundamental."

Peter Fenwick

"The preliminary findings suggest that the people who believe there's nothing instantly, as soon as you die, are probably not correct because the evidence suggests that, at least for the early period of death, mind and consciousness are continuing."

Sam Parnia

How credible, in your view, are these accounts of events when a person seems on the edge of experience between life and death?

What does Peter Fenwick have in mind when he claims that it's "absolutely fundamental" if some people have conscious experience after their brain has ceased to function?

QUESTION 3   QUESTION 4

90 MINUTES IN HEAVEN

"I had the rare and extreme privilege of glimpsing heaven."

Don Piper

To what extent do you find Don Piper's account of being in heaven believable/convincing?

What is the relative importance of such an account in debating the existence of God?

CONCLUDING FROM THE EVIDENCE

"God, being ultimate reality who created us; to miss that is to miss the ultimate purpose for life itself. "

John Lennox

"I don't think I would want there to be a God."

Daniel Dennett

"We have accounts from some people who have been atheists all their lives... and turned at the moment of death to say to their family 'I was wrong' ."

Peter Fenwick

"These are starkly different views of reality."

Chuck Colson

Having viewed this programme – and perhaps others in this series – do you think the evidence suggests that the existence of God is unlikely, probable or certain?

How vigorously would you be prepared to defend your view?

For a summary of *The Case for Theism / The Case for Atheism*, see Appendix 1.

QUESTION 5

QUESTION 6

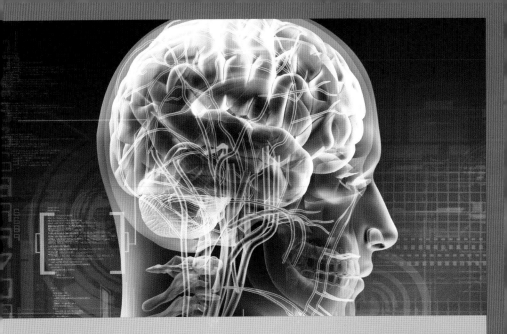

THE CASE FOR THEISM /
THE CASE FOR ATHEISM

IN SUMMARY, CONTEMPORARY SCIENCE HAS REVEALED that the human brain is staggering in its complexity and power. It operates at both a conscious and a subconscious level. It controls every aspect of our physical selves and, in a more mysterious way, is involved in creating our sense of being conscious.

Often a distinction is made between the brain and the mind. Many scientists perceive the mind to be the conscious part of the brain – essentially where our thoughts reside.

But how neurons within the brain produce conscious minds is a deep mystery. Some maintain that the mind might not in fact be produced from the brain but might have a separate existence; the brain is used as a means of transmission, rather like the way TV signals are registered on a television. Such critical issues appear to be highly relevant to the God question, not least of all because of the widespread sense of 'higher consciousness' in human beings.

73

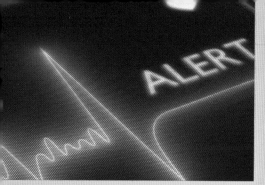

IN SUMMARY, THE CASE FOR THEISM is based on the view that the very existence of human consciousness is a pointer to the existence of the mind of a creator behind the universe. This, in turn, could explain why human beings are essentially 'spiritual' creatures.

Evidence for a creator is also seen in the universality of religion. Granted, there are many differences that could be interpreted as contradictions but it can be argued that the sense of God consciousness that all religions share is more significant than the cultural differences that appear to divide them. Human beings' shared sense of morality is yet another important pointer to their God-connectedness.

The many claims of lives that have been transformed by religious belief provide more evidence of a spiritual, supernatural reality. These personal experiences should be treated very seriously for such transformations can be seen to be a test of Biblical truth. It is a very different test for reality from science which must be seen as only one of many ways of trying to do so. Other forms of evidence also have to be taken very seriously.

Finally, there are thought-provoking accounts of Near Death Experience that, if real, point to human consciousness continuing after clinical brain death. It is feasible that such accounts provide credible scientific evidence that the human mind has a separate existence from the brain.

Considering also the evidence from the cosmos and from the development of life on earth, the reasons for believing in a creator God seem to theists to be substantial and well founded in reason. We can consider ourselves the products of divine intention.

IN SUMMARY, THE CASE FOR ATHEISM is based on the view that, although consciousness is not (so far) convincingly explained by science, the gaps will eventually be filled in.

Evolution, it is argued, has successfully explained the development of life so there is every reason to think that one day evolution will provide a convincing 'naturalist' explanation for the complexity of the human brain, mind and consciousness.

Atheists claim that the origin of mind is in the brain and does not reflect any supernatural consciousness such as God. The only reliable test for truth is science. Explaining a process helps remove the need for any supernatural cause.

Religion is widespread across the world but that appears to be a form of social evolution. Religion has offered some benefits and so has survived. Parents pass on their beliefs to their children and, given that human beings are naturally gullible, religion survives and thrives. Truly rational minds reject religion as superstition. Morality is a product of social evolution.

Transformed lives are explained as a form of self delusion for the real reasons can be found in psychology, not in the reality of God. Near Death Experiences are explained as illusion in a situation where the mind and body are in a highly unusual state of turbulence.

We are here as the result of an exceedingly long, unguided evolutionary process in which all explanations will ultimately be found. Given that our whole universe seems the product of chance, we are the wonderfully fortunate products of a blind and godless system.

APPENDIX 2: UNDERSTANDING THE TERMS

Although every attempt is made to keep scientific explanations as simple as possible, the use of some technical, or less familiar, terms is inevitable.

BELIEF SYSTEM: The answers a person is likely to give to the big questions of life. Where do we come from? What is the meaning of life? Is there life after death?

BRAIN: The organ which is the physical control centre of living beings.

CONSCIOUSNESS: The sense of self awareness and awareness of others and the environment.

HOLY SPIRIT: A form of God that Christians believe can interact directly with human beings: spirit to spirit, mind to mind.

IMMATERIAL: Things which have no obvious physical form.

MATERIAL: Things which have an obvious physical form.

MIND: The cerebral phenomenon in which conscious thinking takes place. Mind is not a phenomenon that can be observed directly. Some scientists claim that the immaterial mind derives from the brain; others suggest that the mind may have its own separate existence but registers its presence through the brain.

NEAR DEATH EXPERIENCE (NDE): A person's conscious sense of experiencing a new reality beyond what is 'normally' experienced in life. Usually it takes place during a period of clinical brain death, with the reports coming from a minority of those who have been resuscitated. The experiences are diverse but often have in common phenomena such as a tunnel, a sense of light and consciousness of the presence of deceased relatives. Whether or not these experiences are 'real' or are more credibly explained as delusional is an open question in science.

NEURON: A brain nerve cell: the building block of the nervous system.

OUT OF BODY EXPERIENCE: As with NDE, the experience is often associated with a period of clinical brain death but in this case the person has a sense of detachment from their body and sometimes reports viewing themselves and those around them from the ceiling.

TRANSCENDENCE: The sense of being connected to a wider reality.

TRUTH (SUBJECTIVE): Beliefs that correspond to reality for individuals; ie make sense to them or are 'true' for them at a particular time. Such truths can vary from individual to individual; eg, John likes coffee (true); Mary likes coffee (not true). Subjective truth can also vary over time: eg, John has toothache (true on Monday but untrue on Tuesday because by then he has visited the dentist).

TRUTH (ABSOLUTE OR OBJECTIVE): Absolutely confirmed fact or reality, based on evidence and standing for all time – perhaps even beyond. Such truths never vary over time or with changing circumstances. Eg, if God definitely exists, that would be an absolute truth. If God does not exist, that would also be an absolute truth.

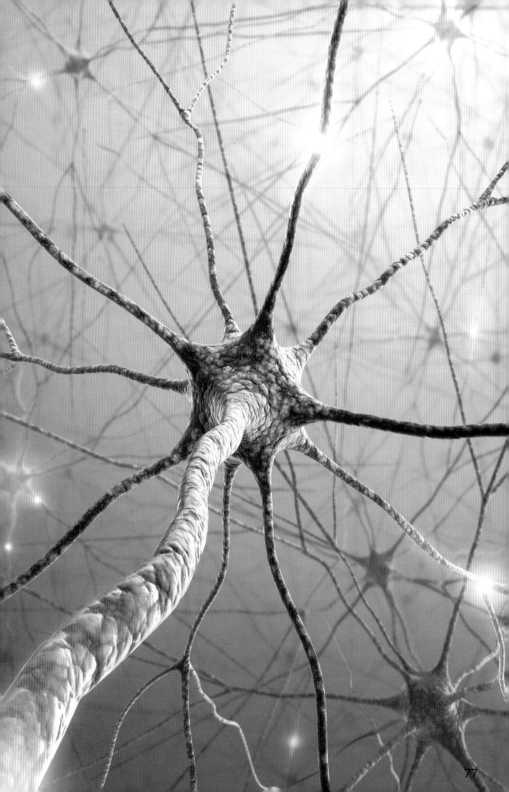

SUGGESTED READING LIST:
A RANGE OF VIEWS

SCIENCE: GENERAL

Bryson, Bill – A Short History of Nearly Everything, Black Swan Books, 2004
Lovelock, James – Gaia : A New Look At Life On Earth, Oxford University Press, 1995
Moore, Pete - The Great Ideas That Shaped Our World, Friedman/Fairfax, 2002
Polkinghorne, John – Quantum Theory: A Very Short Introduction, Oxford University Press 20

THE COSMOS

Cox and Cohen – Wonders of the Universe, HarperCollins, 2011
Davies, Paul – The Goldilocks Enigma, Penguin, 2006
Davies, Paul – The Mind Of God: Science & The Search For Ultimate Meaning, Penguin, 199
Gingerich, Owen – God's Universe, The Belknap Press of Harvard University Press, 2006
Rees, Martin – Just Six Numbers: The Deep Forces That Shape The Universe, Phoenix, 2000
Williams and Hartnett – Dismantling the Big Bang, Master Books, 2005

ORIGIN AND DEVELOPMENT OF LIFE – Understanding Evolution

Alexander, Denis – Creation or Evolution: Do we have to choose? Monarch Books 2008
Dawkins, Richard – The Selfish Gene, Oxford University Press, 1989
Dawkins, Richard – The Greatest Show on Earth: The Evidence for Evolution, Bantam Press, 200
Dennett, Daniel – Darwin's Dangerous Idea, Simon and Schuster, 1995
Miller, Kenneth – Finding Darwin's God: A Scientist's Search for Common Ground
            Between God and Evolution, Harper Perennial, 2007
Ruse, Michael – The Evolution-Creation Struggle, Harvard University Press, 2005
Ruse, Michael – Can A Darwinian Be A Christian? – Cambridge University Press, 2000
Wilson, David Sloan – Evolution for Everyone, Bantam Dell, 2007

ORIGIN AND DEVELOPMENT OF LIFE – Querying Evolution

Behe, Michael – The Edge of Evolution: The Search For The Limits of Darwinism,
            Free Press 2007
Dembski, William – No Free Lunch, Rowman and Littlefield, 2007
Denton, Michael – Evolution: a Theory in Crisis, Adler and Adler, 1986
Findlay, Lloyd, Pattemore, Swift - Debating Darwin: Two Debates – Is Darwinism True
            and Does it Matter? Paternoster, 2009
Fuller, Steve – Dissent over Descent, Icon Books, 2008
Myer, Stephen – Signature In The Cell, HarperOne, 2009
Swift, David - Evolution Under The Microscope, Leighton 2002

ORIGIN AND DEVELOPMENT OF LIFE – Theology and Evolution

Barton & Wilkinson – Reading Genesis after Darwin, Oxford University Press 2009
Berry & Noble – Darwin, Creation and The Fall: Theological Challenges, Apollos, 2009
Lennox, John – Seven Days that Divide the World, Zondervan, 2011
McIntosh, Andy – Genesis For Today, Day One Publications, 1997
Parker, Andrew – The Genesis Enigma: Why the Bible is Scientifically Accurate, Doubleday, 2009
Wilkinson, David – The Message Of Creation, Intervarsity Press , 2002

BRAIN, MIND AND CONSCIOUSNESS

Beauregard and O'Leary – The Spiritual Brain, Harper One, 2007
Dennett, Daniel – Consciousness Explained, Back Bay Books, 1991
Newberg, Andrew – Why We Believe What We Believe, Free Press, 2006
O'Shea, Michael – The Brain: A Very Short Introduction, Oxford University Press 2005
Pinker, Steven – How The Mind Works, Penguin 1997
Piper, Don – 90 Minutes In Heaven, Revell, 2004
Schwartz and Begley – The Mind and the Brain, Harper, 2002

SCIENCE AND GOD: GENERAL

Alexander, Denis – Rebuilding The Matrix: Science and Faith in the 21st Century, Lion, 2001
Alexander and White – Beyond Belief: Science, Faith and Ethical Challenges, Lion, 2004
Andrews, Edgar – Who Made God? EP Books, 2009
Blanchard, John – Does God Believe in Atheists? Evangelical Press, 2000
Collins, Francis – The Language of God, Free Press ,2006
Dawkins, Richard – The God Delusion, Black Swan Books, 2006
D'Souza Dinesh – What's So Great About Christianity, Regnery Publishing, 2007
Gibberson & Collins – The Language of Science and Faith: Straight Answers to
        Genuine Questions, Intervarsity Press, 2011
Harris, Sam – The End of Faith: Religion, Terror and the Future of Reason,
        Simon and Schuster, 2006
Harris, Sam – Letter To A Christian Nation, Bantam Press, 2007
Hitchens, Christopher – God Is Not Great: The Case Against Religion, Atlantic Books, 2007
Houghton, John – The Search For God: Can Science Help? John Ray Initiative, 2007
Keller, Timothy - The Reason for God, Dutton, 2008
Lennox, John – God's Undertaker: Has Science Buried God? Lion, 2007
Lennox, John – God and Stephen Hawking, Lion, 2010
Lennox, John – Gunning for God: Why the New Atheists are Missing the Target, Lion, 2011
McGrath, Alister – Dawkins' God, Blackwell, 2005
McGrath, Alister – Surprised by Meaning, Westminster John Knox Press, 2011
McGrath, Alister – Why God Won't Go Away: Engaging With The New Atheism, SPCK, 2011
Newberg, Andrew – Why God Won't Go Away – Random House, 2001

Polkinghorne and Beale – Questions of Truth: Fifty-One Responses To Questions about
        God, Science and Belief – Westminster John Knox Press, 2009
Robertson, David - The Dawkins Letters: Challenging Atheist Myths,
        Christian Focus, 2007
Ward, Keith – The Big Questions In Science and Religion,
        Templeton Foundation Press, 2008
Ward , Keith – Why There Almost Certainly Is A God, Lion, 2008
Williams, Peter S – A Sceptic's Guide to Atheism, Paternoster, 2009

CHRISTIANITY

Colson, Charles – The Faith, Zondervan, 2008
Colson and Pearcey – How Now Shall We Live? Tyndale House, 1999
Lewis, C S – Mere Christianity, Collins, 1952
Stott, John – Basic Christianity – Intervarsity Press, 1958

USEFUL RESOURCES AND LINKS

A. WEBSITES OF THE SERIES

www.thegodquestion.tv
www.searchfortruthenterprises.com
The links that follow will help you explore further the major topics of the programmes. Most sites listed are supportive of orthodox science but a few challenge accepted scientific paradigms.

B. SCIENCE AND GOD: GENERAL

BioLogos Forum – bioLogos.org
Biologos explores, promotes, and celebrates the integration of science and Christian faith.

Christians in Science – www.cis.org.uk
An international network of those concerned with the relationship between science and Christian faith.

Discovery Institute – www.discovery.org/csc/
Center for Science and Culture.

Faith and Thought – www.faithandthought.org.uk
Relating advances in knowledge to faith within society.

Faraday Institute – www.faraday-institute.org
The Faraday Institute for Science and Religion is an academic research enterprise based at St Edmund's College, Cambridge.

Ian Ramsey Centre (Oxford University) – www.ianramseycentre.org
The Ian Ramsey Centre for Science and Religion conducts research into religious beliefs and theological concepts in relation to the sciences. The Centre is a part of the Theology Faculty at the University of Oxford.

Reasonable Faith – www.reasonablefaith.org
Defending the reasonableness of the Christian faith.

Test of Faith – www.testoffaith.com
Resources on science and faith.

The Centre for Intelligent Design – www.c4id.org.uk
Promoting the design argument.

The Skeptics Society – www.skeptic.com
Testing all claims against scientific criteria.

UCCF – www.bethinking.org
Encouraging the student population to examine the tenets of Christian faith.

C. THE COSMOS

BEYOND: Center for Fundamental Concepts In Science – beyond.asu.edu/drupal/
HUBBLE SITE – Explore Astronomy - hubblesite.org/explore_astronomy/
NASA – www.nasa.gov

D. ORIGIN AND DEVELOPMENT OF LIFE

Understanding Evolution

American Museum Of Natural History – www.amnh.org/
Evolution – www.pbs.org/wgbh/evolution/
Human Origins – humanorigins.si.edu/
Natural History Museum – www.nhm.ac.uk/nature-online/evolution/
The Sedgwick Museum of Earth Sciences, University of Cambridge. –
          www.sedgwickmuseum.org/
Understanding Evolution – evolution.berkeley.edu/

Querying Evolution

Answers In Genesis – www.answersingenesis.org/ - advocating literal interpretations of Genesis
Discovery Institute – www.discovery.org – Advancing a culture of purpose, creativity and
innovation while challenging the adequacy of the Darwinian paradigm

E. BRAIN, MIND AND CONSCIOUSNESS

BBC Science & Nature –
          www.bbc.co.uk/science/humanbody/body/factfiles/brain/brain.shtml

Daniel Dennett Explains Consciousness and Free Will – bigthink.com/ideas/13466

Evidence of the Afterlife Blog – www.netplaces.com/evidence-of-the-afterlife/science-seeks-
an-explanation/the-human-consciousness-project-what-happens-when-we-die.htm

How Stuff Works – www.howstuffworks.com/search.php?terms=brain

Horizon Human Consciousness Project – www.horizonresearch.org/main_page.php?cat_id=47

NDE Research of Suicide – www.near-death.com/experiences/suicide02.html

CONTRIBUTORS' WEBSITES

Most contributors to the series have their own websites. For example:

William Lane Craig – www.reasonablefaith.org
Paul Davies – cosmos.asu.edu
Richard Dawkins – www.richarddawkins.net
Sam Harris – www.samharris.org
Christopher Hitchens – www.dailyhitchens.com
John Lennox – www.johnlennox.org
Mario Livio – www.mariolivio.com
Keith Ward – www.keithward.org.uk

MORE INFORMATION ON CONTRIBUTORS

The God Question series is built largely around scientific evidence and, crucially, the contributors who deliver and often interpret it. Many contributors are among the most eminent in their field. Please consult www.thegodquestion.tv website for pen portraits giving more insight.

UPDATES

Keep checking the website for updates and fresh resource material.

www.thegodquestion.tv/explore